Written by
DORSEY SPENCER JR.

Worms are a Yummy Snack

A story of patience, anger, and joy.

Illustrated by
ANN POMELOVA

I dedicate this book to my son, Chase, who brings me joy. Do what brings you joy and be relentless in pursuit of your dreams and goals!

Acknowledgments

I would like to thank everyone who supported me on this journey. Your words of encouragement have been nourishment for my soul and a primary source of motivation to complete this book. I hope you are proud!

Hardcover: 978-1-7355365-1-4
Paperback: 978-1-7355365-0-7
Ebook: 978-1-7355365-2-1

Library of Congress Number: 2020915254

Edited by Jennifer Rees, RaJhai L. Spencer, Nicole Aghaaliandastjerdi, Chase Spencer, and Tiffani Joi Blunt

Illustrated and Designed by Ann Pomelova

Published by See Us Fly LLC.
SeeUsFly.com

Today is a very special day. Do you know why? No? Okay, I'll tell you. Today I am going on my first fishing trip with my dad! I have been waiting for this day for a long time. This summer, I started a lemonade stand and saved my money so I could buy my very own fishing pole and tackle box.

My dad goes fishing all the time. When he was six years old like me, he learned how to fish with my papa, his dad.

When my dad goes fishing, he brings home all kinds of fish. Silver fish, green fish, flat fish and even fish with whiskers called catfish. Catfish are my favorite... mmm!

Now it's my turn to go and catch some fish. We wake up early in the morning—it still looks like nighttime! We put on our fishing clothes, pack the car, and drive to the ocean.

It seems like it takes forever to get there. I keep asking my dad, "Are we there yet?" Each time, he looks in the rearview mirror with a smile and says, "Be patient, Chase."

Just as I am about to ask for the billionth time,
the car stops and Dad says, "We're here."

"Yay!" I yell, jumping out of my seat.

We get out of the car and smell the cool ocean air. Then, we unload our fishing poles and supplies and begin walking over to the long pier. We walk all the way down to the end and find a nice spot to settle in, where the waves are lapping against the large wooden posts. My dad begins preparing our fishing poles.

He opens the top of a small container that says LIVE BAIT. I look inside and, to my surprise, there are worms crawling all around—lots of them! "Dad, what are we going to do with THOSE?" I ask.

"Worms are a yummy snack for the fish," he says, smiling. "This is how we catch them. Grab one and put it on your hook like this."

"EWWWWW!" I shriek. "I don't want to touch those slimy, grimy worms!" "Do you want to catch fish?" Of course, I want to catch fish. What kind of question is that? I nod my head, yes. "Then you have to touch the worms and put them on your hook. Sometimes we have to do things we don't like to do, in order to do the things we want to do," Dad tells me.

FISH

Slowly, I reach down into the container and grab a worm. It is slippery and keeps wiggling back and forth. "Great job," says Dad, as he helps me put the worm on the hook. Now, we are ready to go. We swing our poles back and then forward and then... plop! Our hooks with the worms are in the water.

Then we wait… and wait… and wait. The waiting seems as long as the ride to the ocean. "How long does this take? I think we have the worms that don't look so yummy and the fish don't want them."

"Just relax and enjoy the moment," Dad says.

"JUST RELAX AND ENJOY THE MOMENT."

I scrunch my face up just like I did when I saw the small container of worms for the first time. What does he mean, relax and enjoy the moment? I want to catch fish! Dad must see the look on my face because he quickly responds, "Use your five senses."

So, I try to do what he says. I look out and far away, I see the ocean meet the sky. I close my eyes and can feel the warm sun on my face. The seagulls' squawking as they fly by fill my ears. I smell the salt in the ocean water, and...

Yank! Yank! "DAD!" I shout. Something is tugging on my fishing pole.
I remember my dad saying something about a fish and a big pull.
The pulling becomes stronger and I get excited.
"I think it's a FISH!!" I say.

My dad holds my arms as I begin to reel in the fish. It becomes harder and harder, but I can feel the fish getting closer. I give a big yank to pull it out of the water and fall backwards on the pier. I bring my pole up... I look at the hook... but there's no fish.

"Looks like he got away!" Dad says.

How could this happen? The fish was right there on my hook. I felt it! I am so angry. I stand up and kick the container of worms.

"Why did you do that? You could have hit someone or hurt yourself," Dad says loudly.

"I'm mad! My fish got away!" I tell him.

He looks at me, takes a deep breath, and says, "Being mad is okay. Hitting things or people because you're mad is not okay. It could be dangerous. If you get mad, take a deep breath, think about why you are mad, and then think about how to fix it. In this case, fixing it is picking up the worms and starting to fish again. Do you understand?"

I think about what Dad says. I waited and waited for that fish. It isn't fair but, I know he is right, so I nod my head, yes.

But then I feel my eyes fill with tears. Dad asks why I am crying. "I thought you were mad at me." Softly, he says, "You made a mistake. We all do. However, it is important to apologize and learn from mistakes, so you don't make the same ones again. I am not mad. I was disappointed, but I still love you very much and always will." I tell him I am sorry. He wipes away my tears, smiles, and gives me a big hug.

"I WAS DISAPPOINTED, BUT I STILL LOVE YOU VERY MUCH AND ALWAYS WILL."

"Now, let's catch us some fish!" Dad says with a sparkle in his eye. He shows me how to put the worm on the hook again, and we start over.

After a short time, there's a slight tug on my fishing pole. Then another and another. Then a big tug. "A fish!" I cry out. I turn the reel and tug away from the water with all of my might, over and over again.

Finally, there is a splash. I lift the hook out of the water and the fish is right there. "I did it! I did it! I caught my first fish!"

"I'm so proud of you, Chase. You didn't give up. Even though you were mad about the other fish getting away, you pulled yourself together and tried again. And look! You caught your first fish. The first of many."

"That was so exciting! I want to catch more!" After the first one, fishing gets way easier. We both catch fish after fish.

"I think that's enough for today. Time to go home," Dad says, and I agree. I am so excited to show my mom and little sister all of the fish we caught.

When we get home, I run into the house and shout, "Mom, look how many fish we caught!" My mom and sister come over and look in the cooler. Mom says, "Wow, that's a lot! You two did well today!"

I say, "Yes, we did, and I caught the first one!"
"Not bad for your first time fishing," Mom says, smiling.

My dad and I put away our fishing poles, then I hurry off to take a shower and change my clothes. I smell like fish, worms, and the ocean!

When I come back downstairs, I see my dad cooking the fish we caught. It smells so good. A short while later, Dad yells, "Dinner is ready!" We all go to the dining room for dinner. We have fish, vegetables, and rice. It is delicious, and it is kind of cool helping with the food we are eating today.

I ask my dad if we can go fishing again tomorrow.
He smiles and says, "No, but how about next weekend?"
"Yes, I can't wait!"

WHAT BRINGS YOU JOY?

CPSIA information can be obtained
at www.ICGtesting.com
Printed in the USA
LVHW071841061222
734685LV00012B/803

* 9 7 8 1 7 3 5 5 3 6 5 1 4 *